Poetry

		DATE DUE	

The Malibu and other Poems

author
Livingston, Myra Cohn

THE MALIBU
AND OTHER
POEMS

THE MALIBU
AND OTHER
POEMS

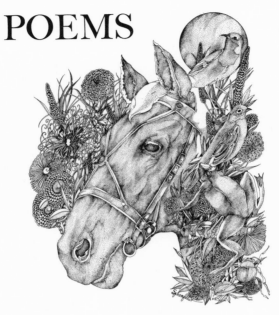

Myra Cohn Livingston

ILLUSTRATED BY *James J. Spanfeller*

A MARGARET K. MC ELDERRY BOOK

Atheneum 1972 *New York*

Text Copyright © 1972 by Myra Cohn Livingston
Illustrations Copyright © 1972 by James J. Spanfeller
Library of Congress catalog card number 72–190557
Published simultaneously in Canada
by McClelland & Stewart, Ltd.
Manufactured in the United States of America
Printed by The Murray Printing Company,
Forge Village, Massachusetts
Bound by H. Wolff, New York
Designed by Harriett Barton
First Edition

To Jascha Heifetz
—for friendship
—for Malibu

Contents

THE MALIBU
AND OTHER
POEMS

Driving

Smooth it feels
        wheels
        in the groove of the gray
            roadway
            speedway
            freeway

long along the in and out
of gray car
   red car
   blue car

catching up and overtaking into
        one lane
        two lane
        three lane

           it feels

over and over and ever and along

Only A Little Litter

Hey moonface,
    man-in-the-moonface,

    do you like the way
    we left your place?

    can you stand the view
    of footprints on you?

    is it fun to stare
    at the flags up there?

    did you notice ours
    with the stripes and stars?

    does it warm you to know
    we love you so?

    moonface,
    man-in-the-moonface,

    thanks a heap for the rocks.

Hear This

Listen, world,
You taught me well.

Taught me to breathe,
to read and spell,
to eat,
to meet   love
             hate
             death

to wait,
to hold my breath

    for peace.

Like It Should Be

There's a blue sky I like.
I really like it.

You don't see much blue anymore.
The smog's too much.

This blue is like the books say,
Blue like they sing about,

Blue like I know it's supposed to be.

Pandora

There's this thing about Pandora's box.
This wondering. This curiosity.
There it was, this box,
Not locked or anything.

And Pandora was bored.

You've heard the rest.
She opened it.
Out came everything bad—
Evil, Famine, Crime, War, Greed
In a great black cloud.

The only joker in the lot
Was Hope.

Get Lost

Look, Gregory, lay off.
Get lost. Get out of here. Lay low.
Get yourself a lake and jump into it.
Get wise and blow.

It's like you can't see, Gregory.
You can't see you're not wanted.
You can't see to go—go—
I want to be alone.

Theme With Variation

rhythm runs
in running
out
and down
around
the
roundabout
of
in
the middle
back to
when
the
rhythm runs
back
in
again

raindrops run
in splashing
out
and down
around
a
roundabout
of
in
the middle
back to
when
the raindrops run
back
in
again

On A Bike

A curve came winding in the road
To make me stop.
I eased the brakes
To slow
    just where the city makes
    its pattern in the earth below.

The eucalyptus leaves blew clean.
I held my breath.
A dusty toad
Bulged gray
    and bulbous in the road.
    Then, next, a darting blue of jay

Streaked past the moment where I stood
In world so blue.
A pile of leaves
Lay dead
    until a crazy breeze
    stirred up the dusty road ahead

And there was someone in a car
Came roaring by.
He slammed his brakes
And cursed
    and asked the road to take.
    "This is the worst

Old mountain road!" he yelled.
The dust flew up.
He started down
The road.
    I watched him head to town
    and looked again to find the toad

And jay. But they had gone.
The place was dry,
All out of tune
And brown.
    "Why waste the whole good afternoon
    up here?" I asked myself, and hurried down.

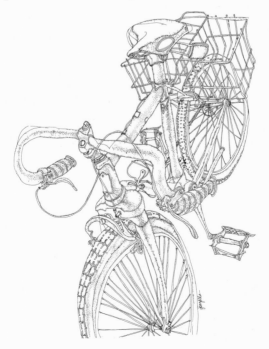

Father

Carrying my world
Your head tops ceilings.
Your shoulders split door frames.
Your back holds up walls.

You are bigger than all sounds of laughter,
of weeping,

Your hand in mine keeps us straight ahead.

The Malibu

You walk it in the winter:
　　it's almost empty.
Oh, someone rides a horse, and the German shepherds
dig and bury their bones in the sand
and a couple of old people drift along
like they're supposed to be walking
and one man plants his fishing pole
to catch himself something for breakfast (ha!)
and all the plants get ideas they can grow
in the winter sand.
　　　　　　　But the roots aren't deep
and all you have to do is give one good
yank and out they come.

Low Tide

Found. One red starfish
at low tide. One
plump, prickly starfish wrested by arm,
by leg, squirming among
purple, bubbling sea urchins.

Plop him in a pail? Scoop up the
salt water? His color will fade.
He will miss his bubbling urchins.

Grab him by the arm. Return him
to his rock, his pink anemone.
One red starfish. Lost.

Grunion

The moon mentions
    the grunion will be running;
    time, she says, to catch them spawning
    silver sand;

    time, she says, to slosh the beach,
    wait for the tide;

    time, she says, to wander the waves,
    spill over, flail,
    reach to the foam,
    watch, wait
    catch
        catch
            catch
                (if you can)

Math Class

She talks about the decimal point,
The reasons why—
But on the window, buzzing free,
A fly

With two red eyes
Moves slowly up the pane.
She moves the decimal one place left
And then again

The fly moves up
And up, practiced and slow.
What I have learned of decimal points
Flies know.

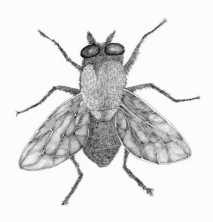

A Book

A book can tell it how it's going
yes
and no

a way of knowing
how
and why
and out-of-sight

in printings
of the
black
on
white

Sycamore

The night the lightning came it sliced the sky
down to the sycamore and tore the trunk in two.
Half-hanging there against the house, it heaved
and all its fuzzy balls rolled out across the
lawn. Great leaves, brown leaves, lay fallen.

The day that Carl came by to take it down
and felled it to the earth I turned my head away.
Still standing there against the house, the stump
keeps watch for all the lightning that may come
again. Sometimes, sometimes, I sit and wait.

Not Mine

Another room
more beautiful
may be.

Still, it would not be mine—

another place
of wood and lace
curtains through shining windows
gathering sun
inside.

But, if I could
for certain
find one—

hide

in its beauty—

still, it would not be mine.

"*For Purple Mountains' Majesty*"

I saw them today.
I saw them.
So many years I have heard them in a song.
It's true. They're purple when you see them.
They rise like kings.
They are mountains.
Suddenly
I know.
I *really* know
What that song is all about.

Texas Norther

I'll buy me a wind today.
It's fall, so why not buy a wind,

a noisy one to stir up my head
and make my arms go round like

branches pushing, my body swaying
like a trunk, an angry wind

with cotton-picking fingers
snatching the old green

of summer, stripping the trees
and chasing dead leaves down the street

to the wind market, at a bargain
price of fifty mph for a blue norther.

12 *October*

From where I stand now
    the world is flat,
    flat out flat,
    no end to that.

    Where my eyes go the land moves out.

    How is it then
    five hundred years ago (about)
    Columbus found
    that far beyond the flat on flat
    the world was round?

German Shepherd

He has never heard of tides,
        of moon and sun
        pulling the water to ebb, to flow.
All that he can know
        is to outrun
        white foam and waves,
        wetting his paws, his muzzle,
        playing the game
        in the joy of a wetness
He can never name   ocean.

Goldfish Whisper

Goldfish whisper
in the blackness of a glass cell:

(Day noises drown their voices)

Oh, I have listened, heard them tell
of endless quiet, lightless night
and its silent secrets.

The Pilgrimage

Think of pilgrims.
The ones who go to sacred places
(A glowing in their faces):
They travel a long, hard road
To see,
To find
            something they feel.

They come to this pilgrimage place,
A shrine, maybe a land.
(A glowing in their faces):
And then they turn home again
And say
I've seen it.
            I've been there.

I've been thinking a lot about pilgrims.
I know the place I want to go to see.
I'm going to tell my family,
How about a place
(A glowing in my face)
            like Disneyland?

It Happened

Well, it happened
(Just like I knew it would).

     I told her once,
     I told her twice,
     I told her never to tell
       a secret to Michelle

         (who can't keep a thing to herself)

And she told her.

And now *everybody* knows!

Sophie E. Schnitter

You wouldn't believe her name—
Sophie E. Schnitter.
The devil-who-gives-peculiar-names
himself must have hit her

with that one. Still,
you have to see her hair,
soft and yellow, and the way
she talks and stands there

and how happy she is, her
smile and red cheeks fit her.
Somehow, you forget she's got a name
like Sophie E. Schnitter.

Punta De Los Lobos Marinos

Remove no object.
No rock, shell,
No chip of ground.
   Here cypress cling,
   Brown kelp beds found
   Swimming with otter,
     Blue overhead
     Flying with gull,
     pelican, cormorant.

Remove no object.
No wildflower,
Branch of pine,
Plant.
   No tidepool treasure mine
   to take away
   to tall shelf
   to shine.

Little Dead

I've buried so many birds,
so many. I've found them dead:
robins, sparrows, feathers red
and brown. Whispered so many words

of what you say soft to birds
who've fallen. I have said
little bird things, little dead-
of-all-small things. My comfort words

won't bring you back, little birds,
to flying. I'll dig a bed
warm and dark to rest your heads
and keep you singing with my words.

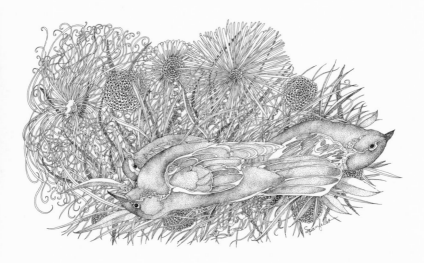

Freeway

The man in the red Ferrari
Zoomed around us
Like we weren't moving.
He just took off,
Gave it the gas,
Practically left us sitting there
On the freeway. And don't you think my
Dad didn't give him a dirty look and
Mumble something about those darned
Little cars.
And
What's wrong with just going normal
Like you're supposed to
At sixty-five mph?

Beginnings

Spring
    happens

    out of the cold.

Winter lives inside your skin

    old
    and
    tight

    then

    buds burst bright

    and you
    begin.

The Way That It's Going

this is the
age of the book
of the book
of the way that
it's going
and where
I
can look for the
yes
and the
no
of a fast-beating
word
and a grab at
tomorrow
and tunes
I have heard in the
picture-frame
white
of the words all in
black
that can push

me to every
tomorrow
and back
to the what-made-me
yesterday
where I can look
and can think
and can wander
alone
in my
book

74th Street

Hey, this little kid gets roller skates.
She puts them on.
She stands up and almost
flops over backwards.
She sticks out a foot like
she's going somewhere and
falls down and
smacks her hand. She
grabs hold of a step to get up and
sticks out the other foot and
slides about six inches and
falls and
skins her knee.

And then, you know what?

She brushes off the dirt and the
blood and puts some
spit on it and then
sticks out the other foot

again.

Time To Practice

Well, here we go again.
The scale of G major with the right hand.
The scale of G major with the left hand.
The scale of G major with both hands together.
Then we can play "The Jolly Millstream"
(as though a piano can sound like a millstream,
if anyone has seen a millstream around this place)
when what we really want to do is to
fool around a little and
figure out how to make some music
sound like one of those concert artists on a
big stage, bounding up and down the keyboard,
and Leonard Bernstein conducting,
and lots of people in the audience applauding
and applauding and applauding.

Here I Am

Here I am, bully,
    Chicken yellow.
I won't fight you.
The last thing to do
Is fight you
With your big red fists and fat cheeks
And mouth like a bursted balloon.

The New One

All your dumb jokes,
I heard them a million times.
I read them in books.

Why don't you find
One I never heard before,
One I never read.

What's black and white and red all over?
That's an old one.
You gonna answer the funny papers?

Forget it.
Get with it.
            A bloody zebra!

Quiet

QUIET

> it says
> in the library

QUIET

> and what I want to know is

> what's quiet
> inside the books
> with all those
> ideas and words

> SHOUTING?

August

Mike says
we ought to have
a swimming party.

Fine, I answer,
but where will we
have this party?

Here, he says,
pointing to the fire hydrant.
Here, he says,
when we turn it on.

We'll have a party
and invite
Alex and
any guy who wants to swim

Stand-
ing
up.

Safety First

Just let old Stan swing by his
   skinny arms on the jungle gym
And shinny up the flagpole five times
And do double flips on the bar.

Me, I don't want to mug myself.

One For Novella Nelson

I like to rest on myself,
   really rest
   and think what's best

   about myself,
   what's wrong
   in the song
   that says I'm alone.

   Me, I'm not alone.
   I've got myself.

Straight Talk (*from a surfer*)

Now here it is   straight
Get up   get up your way
You've got the hang of it
Get up   keep it going

You only go round once in life   kid

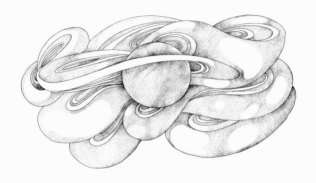

Hokku / Haikai / Haiku

Oh, they found her now,
The moon. She had waited long,
But at last she's found!

Who Needs A Poet?

Who needs a poet?
Who?
Who needs to tell me
    about the blue
    of babbling brooks
    and long lean languishing looks:
    that
    moon rhymes with June
    and a tintinnabular tune

    is mine
    if I will look up at stars
    that shine
    in skies yellow with smog,
    that cat feet of fog,
    the pigeons dying, alas,
    upon the grass—

Who needs a poet
To make *words?*